TANKS
in detail
PzKpfw III Ausf A to N
PANZER III

Above:
Early days. A Panzer III Ausf A with the first type of development suspension undergoing trials. A small number of these tanks took part in the Polish campaign during September 1939. *(TM)*

Left:
Although the suspension arrangements were to change, the Panzer III Ausf A already showed the general appearance and layout that later models were to display. *(TM)*

to be a combat support vehicle for Panzer III formations in the field.

No less than four industrial concerns produced prototypes for the trials that were to lead to the selection of the main production model of the Panzer III. They were Krupps, Rheinmetall-Borsig, MAN and Daimler-Benz. The Daimler-Benz submission was selected but was not ordered into immediate series production for it was apparent that further developmental work still needed to be completed. The early Panzer III thus went through a series of Ausf A, B, C and D models, each with a different suspension system, before the final production form was reached, and even that required some further changes to make it more amenable to mass production.

The main armament for the Panzer III was envisaged as a 5cm high-velocity gun but that part of the Panzer III proposal caused some controversy. In broad terms, a suitable German 5cm gun did not exist during the mid-1930s, although long-term plans existed to develop and manufacture one. At that time a 3.7cm gun was already in established production by Rheinmetall-Borsig for the *Wehrmacht* in the form of the towed *3.7cm PanzerabwehrKanone*

35/36 (3.7cm PaK 35/36), so it made economic and logistic sense to adapt this for tank use. There would then be no need to develop a gun specifically for the Panzer III and the ammunition for the towed gun could be fired from the tank version. During the mid-1930s a 3.7cm gun projectile was still deemed to be capable of penetrating the armour carried by any likely opponent so the Rheinmetall-Borsig gun was accepted for the Panzer III as the *3.7cm KampfwagenKanone* L/46.5 (3.7cm KwK L/46.5).

This was the gun that formed the main armament of the early Panzer III models, at that time sporting the cover name of *Zugführerwagen* (ZW - troop commander's vehicle). There is no need to go into detail regarding these early Panzer III models, especially as this account will concentrate on the heavier-armed models, for they were all very much first attempts. Their armour was thin (only 15mm [0.59in] on the first examples) and their suspension systems proved unsatisfactory. This became apparent with the *PanzerKampfwagen Ausf A* (Ausf - *Ausführung* - model or mark), allotted the ordnance designation of *Sonderkraftfahrzeug 141* (SdKfz 141 - Special Purpose Vehicle 141). Only 15 of this

Ausf A model were manufactured during 1937. They were retained as training vehicles until early 1940.

The same shortcomings were apparent with the developmental Panzer III Ausf B, Ausf C and Ausf D, all of which had limited production runs. By the time the Panzer III Ausf E appeared in late 1938, the suspension had been developed into its final torsion bar form. This Ausf E suspension arrangement, and the general vehicle layout, was retained on all subsequent Panzer III models, differing from that of the Panzer IV mainly by having road wheels each side instead of the eight with leaf springs on the Panzer IV.

Ninety-six examples of the Panzer III Ausf E were manufactured before production switched to the Panzer III Ausf F (still the SdKfz 141). This was basically an Ausf E modified for mass production in hundreds. Until the Ausf E version, all Panzer III production had been carried out by Daimler-Benz at its Berlin-Marienfelde facility. Throughout its development life the Panzer III received very little attention regarding the demands of mass production. As was the German practice at that time, the emphasis was on technical excellence and engineering finesse in detail, with nearly all sub-assemblies and components requiring careful machining and other attentions from skilled workers. The need for speed and ease of production was not then fully appreciated, or was overlooked, in the quest to produce the best technical solutions. By 1939, military staff forecasts predicted that the Panzer III would be required in unprecedented quantities so production line changes had to be introduced to hasten production. Some items were left off while others were simplified. Even after these production modifications had been introduced the Panzer III remained costly in manpower, money and resource terms, as well as being complicated and time-consuming to construct.

Eventually the number of concerns manufacturing the Panzer III and its variants grew to eight. Their details, locations and outputs will be detailed elsewhere in these pages. From late 1940, and the Panzer III Ausf G onwards, the switch to the originally specified 5cm gun took place after combat experience had clearly demonstrated the armour penetration shortcomings of the 3.7cm gun. Thankfully, the turret ring of the early Panzer III models had been made large enough to accommodate the stresses imposed by the larger 5cm guns in both

Above:
A text book illustration of a Panzer III Ausf A. This model was armed with a 3.7cm KwKL/46.5 main gun with two co-axial 7.92mm MG 34 machine guns, plus another in the bow. *(ID)*

Above:
Early Panzer III command vehicles could be identified by their prominent aerial frame array, as seen here on an *Afrika Korps Panzerbefehlswagen III Ausf E*. Note that this example is a conversion as it retains its main armament in a rotating turret . *(TM)*

Right:
The *Panzerbefehlswagen III Ausf D*, still with the developmental form of suspension and with a fixed turret. The aerial frame array is prominent over the hull rear. *(TM)*

Above:
On manoeuvres
with a Panzer III
Ausf E during late
1940. *(HW)*

Left:
Crossing the Meuse
River during the 1940
French campaign,
with the commander
of a Panzer III Ausf E
returning the respects
of one of the combat
engineers responsible
for constructing the
pontoon bridge. *(TM)*

Above:
The Panzer III Ausf B could be identified by its eight pairs of road wheels on each side and the early form of commander's cupola. *(ID)*

Above right:
The Panzer III Ausf D retained the eight pairs of road wheels on each side (with detail suspension improvements) and some armour rearrangements were introduced. A new type of commander's cupola was introduced at the same time. *(ID)*

Below right:
With the Panzer III Ausf E the number of pairs of enlarged road wheels on each side was reduced to six. This remained the definitive suspension format for the remainder of the Panzer III series. *(ID)*

the barrel lengths that became involved (L/42 and then L/60), so the switch could be introduced without undue difficulty. In fact the turret ring installation proved adequate for one further main armament increase, this time to the stumpy 7.5cm low-velocity gun originally carried by the early Panzer IV tanks and *Sturmgeschütz* (StuG) assault gun models.

This latter version of the series, the Panzer III Ausf N (SdKfz 141/2) was the last of the Panzer III tank models, all chassis production after August 1943 subsequently being diverted to production of the *Sturmgeschütz* (StuG), assault gun based on the Panzer III chassis. These vehicles will form the subject of a book later in the Tanks in Detail series.

By the beginning of 1943 the Panzer III series was, at best, obsolescent. New models of combat tank with better armament and protection had overtaken it. There were limits to the numbers of layers of extra armour that could be fitted to the Panzer III, while the diameter limitations of the turret ring precluded any armament increases capable of matching the 75 and 76mm (and larger) guns increasingly installed on Allied tanks.

Yet even after 1943 the Panzer III series remained an important element within the German armoured forces.

CHAPTER TWO

MAIN VARIANTS

The capabilities of the Panzer III were increasingly being reduced by new tanks, such as the Soviet T-34, and the number of options to improve the combat effectiveness of the series became increasingly limited.

Ausf F

Although originally armed with the 3.7cm KwK L/46.5, most examples of the Panzer III Ausf F were later produced or retrofitted with the 5cm KwK L/42, a relatively short-barrelled weapon that was specifically designed as a tank gun. (In addition, some examples of the earlier Ausf E were also retrofitted with the 5cm KwK L/42.)

For the 5cm KwK, the term L/46.5 indicates that the barrel was 46.5 times the calibre in length. Hence the barrel length was 2.325m (7.63ft), its 5cm KwK 39 L/60 successor being 3m (9.84ft) long with enhanced muzzle velocity and armour penetration performance.

Ausf G

The first examples of the Ausf G rolled off the production lines during April 1940. Due to gun production delays, the first 50 or so manufactured retained the 3.7cm KwK L/46.5

and it was these few that saw action in France in May and June 1940. These early examples were later retrofitted with what was meant to be their main armament, the 5cm KwK L/42, when sufficient guns became available. After the first 50 produced, the 5cm L/42 gun was installed as standard at the production stage. Other changes introduced at this stage included the provision of extra armour plates, each 30mm (1.18in) thick, bolted onto all vertical aspects of the hull, including at the rear. The gun mantlet protection was increased to 37mm (1.46in). This additional armour ensured that the overall protection was proof against the projectiles fired by contemporary Allied anti-tank guns up to (and including) the Soviet 45mm Model 1937.

Other changes included a revised visor configuration for the driver, a ventilation fan in the turret roof, and a new type of cupola for the commander. The cupola was the same type as fitted to later models of the Panzer IV. It was initially planned that a total of 1,250 of this model was to be manufactured but this was later reduced to 600, the last of them being delivered during February 1941.

Above:
Newly manufactured Panzer III Ausf G tanks awaiting delivery from the factory. These examples have the newly introduced form of commander's cupola and the third example along has a 5cm KwK L/42 gun. *(TM)*

Left:
A Panzer III Ausf G armed with a 5cm KwK L/42 gun passing a SdKfz 251/6 command vehicle in Thessalonika towards the end of the 1941 campaign in Greece. This tank has been retrofitted with the wider track and new sprocket wheels. *(HW)*

All Ausf G vehicles intended for service in North Africa were provided with extra air filters and revised engine and oil cleaner cooling fan arrangements, either on the production line or retrospectively. They were then known as the Ausf G (Tp), Tp denoting Tropical.

Ausf H

The Ausf H was the first model designed from the outset to carry the 5cm KwK L/42, the turret being reconfigured to accommodate it more comfortably. The bolted-on additional armour plate protection was retained for this model, leading to its replacement on the production lines being introduced earlier than originally planned. When later models appeared with increased unitary armour the Ausf H was superseded. Other changes introduced at the Ausf H stage included a revised transmission, simpler and lighter drive sprockets, and revised idler wheels. Another very practical innovation was the provision of a basket secured to the back of the turret to carry extra equipment and/or crew kit. This basket was gradually retro-fitted to many earlier Panzer III models as well as being a fixture on all subsequent production models.

Above:
On operations in Greece, this example is probably a Panzer III Ausf F. *(BA)*

Left:
Armed with a 5cm KwK L/60 gun, this is a Panzer III Ausf J. This example, fresh off the production lines, still lacks the spaced armour on the hull front. *(ID)*

Ausf I

Although a Panzer III Ausf I is mentioned in some wartime Allied intelligence reports, this designation was not used by the Germans.

Ausf J

From the Panzer III Ausf J onwards the models tended to overlap considerably, due to the introduction of new guns. At the time of its introduction, the relatively short-barrelled 5cm KwK L/42 was seen as an adequate up-gunning solution, introduced into service after the need for something better than the 3.7cm gun became apparent following combat experience in Poland and France. The 5cm KwK L/42 was retained for over half of the production batch of the Ausf J. As this 'over half' batch totalled 1,549, manufactured between March 1941 and July 1942, it was the largest in numerical terms of all models of the Panzer III. The Ausf J was also significant in that it introduced increased armour protection from the outset, with the hull armour being increased to 50mm (1.97in) at the superstructure and hull front. An extra 20mm (0.79in) of *Schottpanzer* (spaced armour

combat disadvantage. It was therefore decided (some accounts mention at Hitler's personal insistence) to introduce the longer-barrelled 5cm KwK 39 L/60 as soon as possible. As only minimal mounting changes had to be made to the mantlet and mounting it was introduced on the existing Ausf J production lines, although some suspension modifications were required at the front of the hull to compensate for the extra weight of the gun and its barrel overhang. To differentiate between the two Ausf J models the ordnance *Sonderkraftfahrzeug* number was revised to SdKfz 141/1 as the ammunition stowage arrangements differed from the earlier version due to the extra length of the 5cm KwK 39 L/60 rounds.

Ausf K

This was the *Panzerbefehlswagen* (command tank) Ausf K described under Variants.

Ausf L

The main change on the Ausf L was the provision of bolt-on spaced armour once again, mainly to the turret and frontal superstructure, to improve protection. The main armament for the Ausf L at first remained the 5cm KwK 39 L/60 but by late 1942 production considerations were being increasingly given to new tank models such as the Panther and later marks of the Panzer IV series. The capabilities of the Panzer III were increasingly being reduced by new Allied tanks, such as the Soviet T-34, and the number of options to improve the combat capabilities of the series became increasingly limited.

After December 1942 the main Ausf L armament was changed once again, this time to the same short-barrelled 7.5cm gun that had been fitted to early models of the Panzer IV series. The Ausf L thus became the Ausf N (see page 24).

All Ausf L vehicles intended for service in North Africa were provided with the same extra air filters and revised engine cooling arrangements as installed on the Ausf G (Tp). They were then known as the Ausf L (Tp).

plating) was later added to the front of the main gun mantlet. Other production changes were single-piece hatches for the driver and radio operator, while the machine gun operated by the latter was provided with a *Kugelblende 30* (ball mounting 30) in place of the original mounting.

In December 1941 a new main gun was introduced to the Ausf J. This was the 5cm KwK 39 L/60, the tank variant of the towed 5cm PaK 38 – both fired the same increased performance ammunition. By late 1941 the German Panzer units were increasingly being confronted by the Soviet T-34 with a 76mm gun, so the Panzer III Ausf J and its forebears were at a distinct

Above:
A captured Panzer III
Ausf E formerly
belonging to the
21st Panzer Division
and fitted with a 5cm
KwK L/42. *(T&A)*

Right:
This illustration of the
same Panzer III Ausf E
shows that the hull
front lacks the spaced
armour added to
many examples once
in service. The tank
carries the white
rhinoceros on a
black background
badge of the British
1st Armoured
Division. *(T&A)*

Above:
A further detail view of the Panzer III Ausf E armed with a 5cm KwK L/42 gun. *(T&A)*

Left:
Top view of the Panzer III Ausf E showing the rear deck layout and also showing the turret basket introduced on the Ausf H and retrofitted to many earlier models. *(T&A)*

Ausf M

The main difference between the Ausf L and the Ausf M was that the latter had provision for optional deep wading equipment (to cross water obstacles up to 1.3m [4.26ft] deep, or 1.5m [4.92ft] with further preparation) with all the inherent sealing and with other engine protection and a new exhaust system. By the time the Ausf M appeared the use of spaced *Schürzen* (skirts) plates along the hull sides and around the turret was becoming standard practice, to give more protection against shaped-charge projectiles. When in place these could obscure vision from the driver's and radio operator's side-mounted vision ports so these were omitted during production. Another measure to speed production at this stage was the elimination of the hull escape hatches. Other innovations introduced at the Ausf M stage included a revised engine exhaust pipe and silencer arrangement to reduce the exhaust signature at night.

Another option in increasingly widespread use on the Eastern Front was the so-called *Ostketten*, or East tracks. These were wider (and heavier) than the standard tracks to partially reduce the ground pressure when travelling over muddy or soft terrain, adding to the overall vehicle width already increased by the installation of *Schürzen*.

Above:
A detail view of a Panzer III Ausf M. Note the vision port on the turret side has been deleted. Also that smoke grenade launchers have been fitted. *(ID)*

Above left:
The long, slender barrel of the 5cm KwK L/60 main gun and spaced frontal armour indicates that this is a Panzer III Ausf J; the Ausf L was visually similar apart from the absence of spaced armour. *(ID)*

Left:
A Panzer III Ausf G deployed with the *Afrika Korps* 'somewhere in the Western Desert' of North Africa during late 1941. The late production Ausf G was armed with a 5cm KwK L/42 gun. *(TM)*

Above:
Perhaps the most
easily recognisable
variant of the Panzer
III series was the
Panzer III Ausf N,
thanks to the stubby
7.5cm KwK 37 L/24
close support gun. *(ID)*

Right:
One of many Panzer III
tank series variants
was the *Pionierpanzer
III* carrying various
items of combat
engineer equipment
such as these combat
bridges. These
vehicles, and various
other carriers, were
created by employing
redundant turretless
Panzer III tank chassis
and hulls. *(HW)*

In the event, production of the Ausf M as a high-velocity gun tank was destined to be terminated after February 1943. By that time the Panzer III series was increasingly being assessed as obsolescent as gun tanks but the same 7.5cm up-gunning procedures as for the Ausf L could still apply. The last of the batch originally scheduled to be completed as Ausf M models were therefore produced as the Ausf N. Later a further batch of 100 examples of the Ausf M was completed as *Flammenwerfer* (Fl - flamethrower) tanks and they are described separately under Variants.

Ausf N

The Panzer III Ausf N (SdKfz 141/2) was destined to be the last of the Panzer III gun tank series. Its main armament was the 7.5cm KwK 37 L/24 close-support gun firing high-explosive or armour-penetrating shaped-charge projectiles, as originally installed on all Panzer IV models up to the Ausf F1 and also on the early versions of the

Sturmgeschütz assault gun series. Many of the 7.5cm guns involved in the Ausf N programme were in fact taken from retired examples of the Panzer IV.

The Ausf N carried over most of the features of the late Panzer III production models, with examples constructed using features of the Ausf J (3), Ausf L (447) and Ausf M (213). In addition, 37 earlier Panzer III models were completely rebuilt to Ausf N standard, making exactly 700 examples in total.

As well as assuming some of the *Sicherheits-panzer* (close-support tank) combat duties formerly undertaken by early models of the Panzer IV series, the Panzer III Ausf N was also deployed within Tiger I tank units to provide close-range fire support.

The Ausf N proved to be remarkably successful in its *Sicherheitspanzer* role, even if the gun's anti-armour capabilities were somewhat limited. The last of them was delivered in August 1943, after which all Panzer III tank production ceased. Other more pressing tank production priorities had intruded.

CHAPTER THREE

PzKpfw III Ausf M

All Panzer III tanks were time-consuming to produce, being constructed from many armoured steel plates welded together. The superstructure alone was made up from 11 plates, thus making costly production.

The crew for all Panzer III models was five, the same as for the larger Panzer IV. As with the Panzer IV they were the commander, gunner and loader in the turret, and the driver in the hull (on the left, facing the front) with the radio operator/machine gunner seated to his right.

The hull and turret were fabricated using high-quality chromium-molybdenum steel plates welded or bolted together. The total weight of armour plate for the Ausf L (turret and hull and excluding ports, hatches, etc) was 6,091kg (approx 6 tons), with thicknesses as follows:

Hull front –	50mm (1.97in)
Hull sides –	30mm (1.18in)
Hull rear –	50mm (1.97in)
Hull bottom	16mm (0.63in)
Superstructure front –	50mm + 20mm
	(1.97in + 0.79in)
Superstructure sides	30mm (1.18in)
Superstructure rear	50mm (1.97in)
Superstructure top	18mm (0.71in)
Engine covers	17mm (0.67in)
Turret front	57mm (2.25in)
Turret sides	30mm (1.18in)

Turret rear –	10mm (0.39in)
Gun mantlet	50mm + 20mm
	(1.97in + 0.79in)
Schürzen –	8mm (0.32in [hull])*
	5mm ([0.20in turret])*
	*If installed.

Extra frontal protection could be obtained by carrying spare track lengths across the front of the hull and front superstructure plate. From 1943 onwards, further protection against magnetically-applied shaped charges could be provided by a liberal coating of *Zimmerit* anti-magnetic paste; a single Panzer III required 100kg (220.1lb) of this for a full coating, which was also applied to the *Schürzen*, if installed.

To ease production each vehicle was formed from four pre-fabricated sub-assembles: hull, turret, front superstructure and rear super-structure. The main sub-assembly was the hull, manufactured from armoured plates and forming an armoured shell onto which the superstructure was placed. The main superstructure, formed from 11 plates, carried the turret while the rear superstructure covered the engine compartment.

Above:
This group of fully equipped late production Panzer III Ausf N close support tanks was surrendered to the Allies in Norway in 1945. The long gun barrel of a Panzer III Ausf J, L or M can be seen in the centre of the group. *(TM)*

Left:
Complete with dummy gun to the right of its centrally mounted MG34 machine gun, is this *Panzerbefehlswagen Ausf E. (TM)*

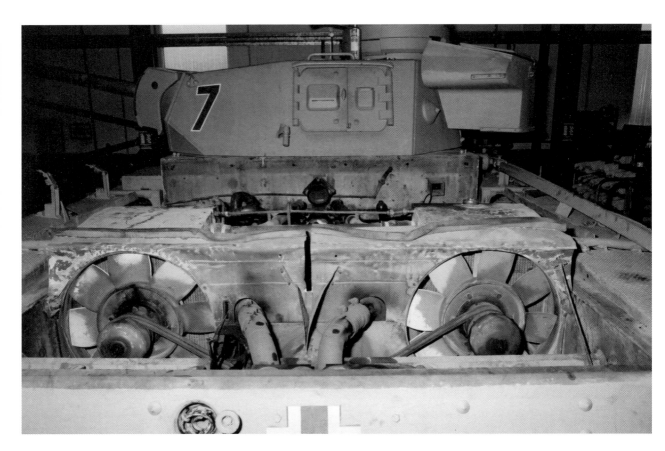

Above:
Water cooling was achieved by two engine-driven fans which drew air from the louvres over the engine compartment and through the radiators. *(TM)*

At the front of the hull were two compartments — the fighting compartment and the engine bay — separated by a bulkhead, with the front of the engine compartment containing the gearbox and steering mechanism. Two hinged doors over the hull front plate provided access to the brake mechanisms and also acted as escape hatches for the driver and radio operator. Further front-hinged doors for escape purposes were located centrally, one in each of the hull sides on all Panzer III models up to the Ausf M, when they were eliminated to speed production. Thanks to this hatch elimination the number of 5cm KwK 39 L/60 rounds carried could be increased from 84 to 92. (Late production Ausf L models also had the side doors removed.)

The superstructure front vertical plate mounted the driver's visor behind a *Fahrerblende 30* armoured cover, and a *Kugelblende 30* ball-mounting for the hull machine gun. Vision blocks with armoured covers were provided for both the driver and radio operator. The driver was also provided with a *Kampfwagenfahrerfernrohr 2* (KFF2) episcope vision device with a field of view of 63° and x1 magnification.

The radio installed was the *FunkSprech-Gerät 5* (FuSprGer 5), the standard Panzer unit communication link. It had a transmitter output of 10 Watts and a speech range under normal conditions of 2km (1.24 miles). The set used a 2m (6.56ft) long whip antenna which, when travelling, was stowed hinged down into a long protective housing. The location of this housing varied from model to model but was usually on the right of the superstructure with the antenna folding to the rear.

The turret was of all-welded construction and was visually similar to that of the Panzer IV but smaller. (An attempt to mount a Panzer IV turret on a Panzer III proved unsuccessful as the extra weight of the turret proved excessive.) The gunner was seated to the left of the gun while the commander was located centrally towards the rear. Both these crew members had their seats secured to the turret so that they rotated with it. The third occupant of the turret, the loader, had no seat while in action as he stood to the right-hand side of the breech. Hinged double doors were provided in each turret side wall, doubling as loading or escape hatches. The doors had vision ports, with a further two ports in the mantlet

front. Armoured flaps covered all these ports. Two pistol ports were located in the rear turret wall. The bottom contours of the external turret basket, used for extra equipment and crew kit stowage, were curved to permit as wide a field of fire as possible for these two pistol ports.

The turret roof had the commander's cupola mounted centrally. From the Ausf G onwards this was the same type as mounted on the Panzer IV so it had armour from 50mm (1.97in) to 95mm (3.74in) thick and five vision slots protected by armoured shutters. Two semi-circular hatch covers provided access through the cupola. The turret roof also had an extractor fan cowl and a signal port through which a 27mm signal flare pistol could be fired. This signal port was to the front left of the cupola.

The engine compartment, separated from the combat compartment by a bulkhead, was located to the rear of the hull under armoured covers over the superstructure. Louvres were provided to permit cooling air to be drawn into the engine compartment with further air entering through side intakes covered with wire mesh grids. The air passed over the engine to two radiators cooled by two belt-driven fans. Two Mahle oil bath air

filters (four up to the Ausf J) were located over the engine. All the air intakes were covered by steel shutters that were normally held open. When they had to be closed when negotiating water obstacles, cable controls released the shutter latches and they were closed by springs.

The engine was a V-12 Maybach 120 TRM, a water-cooled petrol unit with a capacity of 11,867cc. It developed 300hp at 3,000rpm and was developed specifically for the Panzer III series. (In some German accounts the engine output is given as 265hp at 2,600rpm.) Although this engine was a Maybach design it was also licence-produced by other manufacturers.

The usual maximum fuel capacity was 310ltr (68.2gal), sufficient for a road range of approximately 145 to 155km (90 to 96miles). Cross country the range was about 95km (approx 153 miles). Extra fuel could be carried in an auxiliary tank carried over the rear of the vehicle, although it appears that this option was not often employed.

Power from the engine was transmitted forwards through a Cardan shaft to the hydraulically controlled clutch on the gearbox located at the front of the vehicle - the engine and

Above:
The V12 Maybach 120TRM water-cooled engine fitted in the tight confines of the Panzer III engine compartment. The designation TRM was for *Trockensumpf-schmierung mit Schnappermagnet* - dry sump lubrication with impulse magneto. *(TM)*

Specifications - Panzer III Ausf M

			Range, road:	155km	(96 miles)
			Fording:	unprepared, 1.3m	(4.27ft)
Crew:	5 (commander, driver, main gunner,		Vertical obstacle:	600mm	(1.97ft)
	bow machine gunner/radio operator,		Trench crossing width:	2.2m	(7.23ft)
	loader)		Gradient:	30°	
Weight in combat:	21,130kg	(20.8 tons)	Engine:	11,867cc V-12 Maybach HL 120 TRM	
Length, overall:	6.55m	(21.49ft)		water-cooled petrol developing	
Length, hull:	5.78m	(18.96ft)		300bhp at 3,000rpm	
Width:	2.97m	(9.74ft)	Transmission:	ZF Aphon SSG77WrA 705 six	
Width with Schürzen:	3.41m	(11.19ft)		forward and one reverse gears	
Height:	overall, 2.5m	(8.2ft)	Steering:	clutch and brake	
Track:	2.51m	(8.23ft)	Suspension:	torsion bar	
Track width:	400mm	(15.76in)	Electrical system:	12V	
Ground clearance:	385mm	(1.276ft)	**Armament:**		
Max speed, road:	40km/h	(25mph)		1 x 5cm KwK 39 L/60 gun	
Fuel capacity:	310ltr	(68gal)		2 x 7.92mm MG 34 machine guns	

Left:
An early production
Panzer III Ausf N
moving up to a
position 'somewhere
in the Soviet Union',
probably during early
1943. *(TM)*

side. A hydraulically assisted steering system was integrated in the gearbox with the Daimler-Benz/Wilson clutch/brake system employing brakes attached to the hull side plates. Both track brake systems were independently hydraulically operated from two steering levers operated by the driver.

Each track consisted of 93 cast manganese steel track plates each 400mm (15.76in) wide, although the track width on early models was 360mm (14.2in). Wider *Ostkette* tracks were available for use on the Eastern Front (apparently they were not often used). Extra steel teeth could be secured through the track plates to improve the surface grip during operations under icy conditions. Track tension was adjusted using a lever to alter the position of the rear idler wheel. Three pairs of return rollers were provided each side.

Six pairs of rubber-tyred road wheels were provided each side, with pairs of spares carried over the rear of the engine covers. Further spare wheels were often carried along the left-hand side of the vehicle, over the track covers.

The suspension was devised by Dr Ferdinand Porsche and employed lateral torsion bars, the front and rear four bars being 55mm (2.17in) in diameter while the centre four bars were 44mm (1.73in) thick. Shock absorbers were provided for the front and rear wheels. As the bars were arranged side-by-side to save space inside the hull, the road wheels were staggered by 127mm (approx 5in). The torsion bar swinging arms acted rearwards on the left-hand side and forward on the right.

The 12V electrical system was powered from a Bosch GTLN 600/12 generator with a 70A output capacity. The usual starter was an electric 4 hp Bosch BNG 4/24 ARS 129 motor with backup from an AL/ZMA/R 4 hand starter. Power was stored in four 12V, 105A batteries.

To assist starting under the low temperature conditions of the Eastern Front, the Panzer III Ausf M introduced an engine pre-heating system also employed on the Panzer IV Ausf G onwards. For this, warm air and engine coolant from an already-running vehicle were circulated around the cold unstarted engine, the two vehicles located back-to-back. After about 10 to 15 minutes of warming the cold engine could then be started safely with a reduced risk of cold-induced damage.

According to scrupulous German accountants, each Panzer III Ausf M cost the Third Reich exactly Reichmark (RM) 96,163, without the armament and other equipment.

gearbox were not directly in line with each other as the gearbox was set slightly to the right of centre. Control of the transmission was effected through a vacuum-operated selector and gear change system using a pre-selector lever. A further hand lever selected forward or reverse drives. On early Panzer III models the Maybach Variorex gearbox provided 10 forward and four reverse gears but experience demonstrated that such a ratio selection was not necessary. For instance, only one reverse gear was ever used so from the Ausf H onwards only that one was provided by the installation of a Zahnradfabrik Friedrichshafen Aktiengesellschaft (ZF) Aphon SSG77WrA 705 pre-selector gearbox and the number of forward gears was reduced to six. Power was taken from the gearbox through short drive shafts and via epicyclic gears to the external drive sprocket each

economic and logistic reasons by the ready availability of the 3.7cm KwK L/46.5 that seemed to be perfectly adequate for the foreseeable future. Once it was appreciated that the 3.7cm gun was no longer viable a change to 5cm had to be made.

Fortunately for the Panzer III crews, such a gun had been under development since 1936, when Rheinmetall-Borsig began developing a 5cm 42-calibre gun specifically for tanks, soon known as the 5cm KwK L/42. For a tank gun the 5cm KwK L/42 had a relatively short barrel but at the time of its introduction into service by the end of 1940 it, in its turn, was deemed adequate against any targets it was likely to encounter. That complacency was soon shattered.

The 5cm KwK L/42 fired a solid steel armour-piercing projectile, the *5cm Panzer-granate 39* (5cm Pzgr 39) weighing 2.06kg (4.54lb), at a muzzle velocity of 685m/sec (2,247ft/sec). It could defeat 46mm (1.81in) of armour at 500m (546.8yd), compared to 34mm (1.34in) by the 3.7cm gun at the same range. Also available was an AP40 equivalent, the 5cm Pzgr 40, which remained in production on a declining scale until 1942. The projectile for this round weighed 9259g (2.04lb) and was fired at a muzzle velocity of 1,060m/sec (3,478ft/sec). It could defeat 58mm (2.29in) of armour at 500m (546.8yd) although, being lighter, its velocity and striking power diminished soon after this distance, beyond which the Pzgr 39 proved superior. This loss of Pzgr 40 performance at extended ranges meant that the Pzgr 39 was usually the preferred option, something reinforced by the already mentioned tungsten shortages causing AP40 supply problems. A high-explosive projectile (the *5cm Sprenggranate 38*) weighing 1.82kg (4lb) was also available for the conventional fire support role. The muzzle velocity for this latter round was 550m/sec (1,804ft/sec).

The 5cm KwK L/42 was introduced from the Panzer III Ausf G onwards, simply by replacing the 3.7cm gun and its internal mantlet by the 5cm KwK L/42 with its external mantlet. The turret ring diameter of 1.524m (5ft) meant that it was of adequate size to accommodate the increased recoil stresses produced by the more powerful gun. Replacement was so straight-forward that many examples of the Panzer III Ausf E and Ausf F were subsequently retrofitted with the 5cm KwK L/42 to prolong their service lives. By late 1941, 3.7cm gunned tanks were no longer in the front line, although it appears that some were still listed in German inventory documents as late as September 1944, no doubt in the training role.

Above:
Turret top detail of a Panzer III Ausf E with the 3.7cm KwK L/46.5 gun still in its original form of mantlet. Extra armour plate has been welded on as an 'in the field' improvement, for increased protection. *(TM)*

Above:
A mounting for the
7.92mm MG34
was produced to
fit on the front of
the commander's
cupola. Note the
canvas bag for the
ammunition which
was stowed inside
the tank (see
page 42). *(TM)*

Right:
Rear view of a
Panzer III Ausf E
commander's
cupola. Note the
pistol port
covers in the rear
turret wall, easily seen
as this example lacks
the turret basket
introduced as
standard on the
Panzer III Ausf H. *(TM)*

Above:
The interior of the gunner's door in the turret side of a Panzer III series tank showing the vision device and pistol port aperture. *(TM)*

Left:
The exterior of the gunner's door in the turret side of a Panzer III series tank. *(TM)*

The Panzer III models armed with the 5cm KwK L/42 carried 99 rounds. The gun had a semi-automatic, vertical sliding breech block and was fired electrically. The gunner's sight was a *Turmzielfernrohr 5aver1* (TZF 5aver1), a 2.4-magnification telescope having a field of view of 25° and calibrated for ranges up to 2,000m (2,187.2yd).

The adequacy of the 5cm KwK L/42 did not last very long. Soon after the German invasion of the Soviet Union the German Panzer units encountered their first T-34 tanks. With their 76mm guns and thick sloped armour the T-34s were formidable opponents for the Panzer III units

as their 50mm L/42 guns could inflict damage only at short ranges or by a lucky shot. The very appearance of the T-34 rendered almost the entire German tank inventory obsolete but measures had to be taken to keep them in the field.

This entailed another new main gun for the Panzer III. Once again Rheinmetall-Borsig came to the rescue for it had been developing a more powerful 5cm gun in tandem with the 5cm KwK L/42 since 1936. Intended for towed use, this gun had a longer L/60 barrel, creating a higher muzzle velocity, and thus more on-target impact than the L/42, while retaining the same projectiles as before coupled with more powerful

propellant charges in longer cartridge cases. The towed gun became the 5cm PaK 38, although it was 1940 before the troops obtained the first of them. Thereafter the 5cm PaK 38 was in great demand for it proved to be the only gun capable of having any chance of knocking out T-34 tanks at combat ranges.

As the L/60 ordnance was a close relative of the L/42 gun it could be installed in what was virtually the same mounting and mantlet, although some changes were made to the recoil mechanism. Another change was to the barrel preponderance compensator, changed from a coiled spring arrangement to a torsion bar.

Firing the same Pzgr 39 ammunition as the 5cm KwK L/42, the 5cm KwK 39 L/60 had a muzzle velocity of 835m/sec (2,739ft/sec). It could penetrate 59mm (2.33in) of armour at 500m (546.8yd) or 48mm (1.89in) at 1,000m (1,093.6yd). When Pzgr 40 (AP40) ammunition was available it had a muzzle velocity of 1,180m/sec (3,871ft/sec) and could penetrate 72mm (2.84in) of armour at 500m (546.8yd). The high-explosive *5cm Sprenggranate 38* projectile was also retained, its muzzle velocity remaining the same at 550m/sec (1,804ft/sec).

In theory, and in addition to the ammunition types mentioned above, the 5cm KwK 39 L/60

Right:
The hull machine
gunner's position on
a Panzer III Ausf L.
Note the canvas
ammunition bags for
the MG 34 in their
stowage. *(TM)*

could utilise a special muzzle-launched, shaped charge, anti-armour or strongpoint demolition projectile. This was the fin-stabilised *Stielgranate 42*, a short-range, direct-fire projectile weighing 13.5kg (29.76lb) that could penetrate up to 180mm (7.09in) of armour. Firing involved a special blank charge loaded into the chamber, producing a muzzle velocity of 180m/sec (590ft/sec). It was little used.

Despite the heavy demands for the towed 5cm PaK 38, the tank version, the 5cm KwK 39 L/60, appeared during 1940 and was soon in equal demand. Apart from mounting details, the tank gun was the same as the towed gun and

had the same overall performance, although the KwK 39 L/60 version did not have a muzzle brake. The first Panzer III model to receive the 5cm KwK 39 L/60 was the late production Ausf J (SdKfz 141/1). It remained the operational Panzer III gun until the Ausf N appeared.

Due to the longer cartridge cases involved, the late production Panzer III Ausf J models armed with the 5cm KwK 39 L/60 had their ammunition stowage capacity reduced to 84 rounds. Following the elimination of the hull side escape doors on the late production Ausf L and the Ausf M, their ammunition stowage capacity was increased to 92 rounds. The gun had a semi-

Left:
Close-up detail of the optical sight and the gunner's traverse and elevation control inside a Panzer III series tank. The firing trigger can be seen on the lower wheel used for manual traverse changes. The turret position indicator, marked in 1-12 divisions, can be clearly seen. The sight in this tank is not fitted with the brow pad seen on pages 40 and 41. *(TM)*

automatic, vertical sliding breech block. The 5cm KwK 39 L/60 was fired electrically while the towed 5cm PaK 38 was fired by percussion, so its ammunition differed in that respect. The gunner's sight was a TZF5b 2.4 magnification telescope having a field of view of 25° and calibrated for ranges up to 3,000m (3,281yd).

For the record, the 5cm KwK 39 L/60 was 3m (9.84ft) long and weighed approximately 435kg (959lb) without its mounting. This weight meant that some slight changes had to be made to the front suspension arms to compensate for the extra forward weight. As mounted in the late model Panzer III turrets the maximum angle of

barrel elevation was +20°, with depression being -10°. The maximum possible rate of fire from a trained crew was up to 15 shots in one minute, although this rate was seldom necessary under combat conditions.

Also for the record, each 5cm KwK 39 L/60 cost the Third Reich a nominal RM 5,000.

The last model of the Panzer III series was the Ausf N. As previously mentioned this carried a short-barrelled close fire support gun, the 7.5cm KwK L/24. This was a Krupp-manufactured gun originally developed for early models of the Panzer IV tank and *Sturmgeschütz* assault guns. In fact some, perhaps all, the guns installed in

the Ausf N were transferred from these otherwise obsolete vehicles.

The 7.5cm KwK L/24 (actual calibre length L/23.5) was a low-velocity gun weighing 490kg (1,080.25lb) without its mounting. It had the usual Hotchkiss-type semi-automatic, vertical-sliding breech block and was fired electrically. It was primarily a fire support weapon since its low muzzle velocity meant it was more effective when firing high explosive rather than armour-piercing projectiles. Since the main role for the gun was close fire support, armour penetration was thus secondary. In theory, an ammunition load was meant to be 65% high explosive, 25% armour piercing and the remaining 10% screening or marker smoke. In practice the mix was altered to suit the anticipated mission. The Panzer III Ausf N had stowage for 64 rounds of 7.5cm ammunition.

Several models of anti-armour round were developed for the 7.5cm KwK L/24. The least effective was the 7.5cm *Kanone Granaterot-Panzer*. This hardened steel projectile weighed 6.8kg (14.99lb) and was fired at a muzzle velocity of

385m/sec (1,263ft/sec). Despite its weight the armour penetration at 500m (546.8yd) was just 39mm (1.54in).

Slightly better in armour penetration terms was a series of 7.5cm shaped-charge projectiles. When they were first introduced, shaped charge projectiles seemed to offer great advances in armour penetration and they worked well under laboratory conditions. In practice the results were disappointing as the high-temperature jet, produced by the warhead to burn through target armour, was dispersed and reduced in effect by projectile spin. Only one of these shaped charge projectiles needs to be considered here, the *7.5cm GranatePatrone 38 H1/C*, although there were others. The projectile for this round weighed 4.8kg (10.58lb), fired at a muzzle velocity of 450m/sec (1,476ft/sec). Theoretically it could penetrate 90mm (3.55in) of armour at any combat range, thanks to its shaped charge capabilities which were not supposed to alter with range.

The usual high-explosive projectile was the *7.5cm Granate 34* with a maximum possible

It should be noted that the above were completion centres supplied with components and sub-assemblies provided by numerous smaller concerns and sub-contractors. For instance, hulls, superstructures and turrets were mainly supplied by the Deutsche Edelstahlwerke AG of Hannover. The main armament was largely a Rheinmetall-Borsig responsibility, although most of the 5cm guns were supplied either from Karges–Hammer of Braunschweig or Franz Garny of Frankfurt, both of them subsidiaries of Rheinmetall-Borsig.

Not all the above-mentioned manufacturers were involved in the production of every model. Their involvement was as follows:

Daimler-Benz	Ausf E, F, G, J, L
ALKETT	Ausf F, G, H, J, L
FAMO	Ausf F, G
Henschel	Ausf E, F, G, H, J, L, N
MAN	Ausf E, F, G, H, J, L, M, N
MIAG	Ausf H, J, L, M, N
MNH	Ausf G, H, J, L, M, N
Wegmann	Ausf G, H, J, L, M, N

Doubtless a great deal of delving could determine exactly how many of each model were manufactured by each concern but the following table provides an overview of the annual totals specified by their main armament (below):

	1939	1940	1941	1942	1943	1944
Panzer III, 3.7cm KwK	157	396	-	-	-	-
Panzer III, 5cm KwK L/42	-	466	1,649	251	-	-
Panzer III 5cm KwK 39 L/60	-	-	64	1,907	22	-
Panzer III 7.5cm KwK L/24	-	-	-	449	213	-

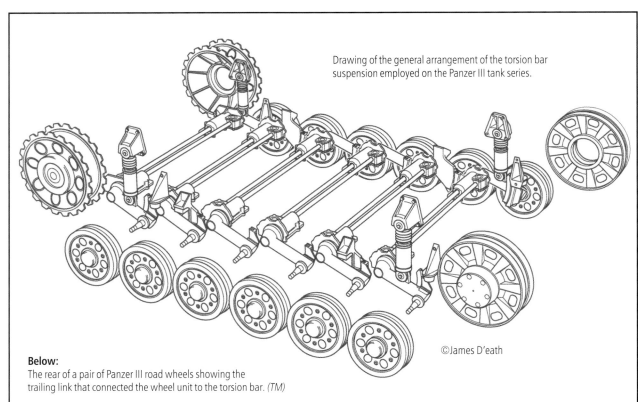

Drawing of the general arrangement of the torsion bar suspension employed on the Panzer III tank series.

©James D'eath

Below:
The rear of a pair of Panzer III road wheels showing the trailing link that connected the wheel unit to the torsion bar. *(TM)*

Above:
Detail of the rear deck of a Panzer III Ausf J showing the provision of chequered plates to improve foothold and prevent crew members from slipping during maintenance and general access. *(TM)*

Left:
This illustration shows the small, hull side escape hatch provided on all Panzer III models up to about mid-way through the Ausf L production run. It was then deleted to speed production. *(TM)*

The production totals for each tank gun model were as follows:

Panzer III Ausf E	96
Panzer III Ausf F	435
Panzer III Ausf G	600
Panzer III Ausf H	308
Panzer III Ausf J	1,549
Panzer III Ausf J (SdKfz 141/1)	1,067
Panzer III Ausf L	653
Panzer III Ausf M	250
Panzer III Ausf N	700 *

*Includes 37 remanufactured vehicles.

Inevitably, the annual and model totals do not coincide, almost certainly due to battle-weary vehicles being remanufactured to later model standards or due to end-of-model production runs being transferred to other model standards. Typical examples of this was the diversion of various model chassis to boost the numbers of Ausf N 75mm gun tanks and the diversion of 100 Ausf M chassis to be converted to Panzer III (Fl) flamethrower tanks (see under Variants). Production or diversion of some models as command vehicles adds further confusion.

For the record the allotted chassis numbers given to each individual chassis were as follows, by model:

Panzer III Ausf E	60401-60496
Panzer III Ausf F	61001-61650
Panzer III Ausf G	65001-65950
Panzer III Ausf H	66001-66650
Panzer III Ausf J	68001-69000
Panzer III Ausf J (SdKfz 141/1)	72001-74100
Panzer III Ausf L	74101-75500
Panzer III Ausf M	76101-77800
Panzer III Ausf N	73851-77800.

Above:
A short length of Panzer III series track demonstrating how the individual track shoes were connected together. *(TM)*

Above left:
View from the front of a Panzer III series tank showing how the track shoes interacted with the drive sprocket. *(TM)*

Below left:
A view from the inside of a Panzer III series track shoe clearly showing the central track guide and the connecting pin. *(TM)*

Right:
Looking upwards into the commander's cupola on a Panzer III series tank. Pads to protect the commander's face can be seen between the vision blocks. The handle under each block operated the sliding armour cover outside it. *(TM)*

Below:
By the end of the war Schürzen spaced-armour plates intended to provide extra protection against shaped charge armour penetrating warhead were a frequent combat accessory. Applied to both hull sides and the turret, the thin steel plates could be easily damaged or become lost altogether, as seen on this Panzer III Ausf L or M. *(TM)*

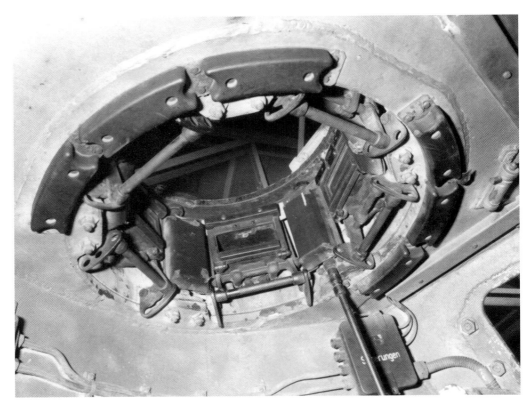

Above:
Factory new *Artillerie-Panzerbeobachtungs-wagen* armoured artillery observation vehicle based on a Panzer III Ausf F tank. *(TM)*

Left:
Head on view of a *Panzerbefehlswagen* command tank based on a Panzer III Ausf F. Note the star array aerial behind the commander. *(HW)*

'standard' Panzer III suspension. A total of 45 of the latter were manufactured at a slow rate from July 1939 until February 1940, again by Daimler-Benz. In addition to the two radio suite options already provided with the Ausf D[1] model, a further Ausf E (SdKfz 266) variant carried a FuSprGer 2 radio as well as the command net FuSprGer 6. The FuSprGer 2, a receive-only equipment, allowed commanders to know what was going on within a range of 4km (2.49miles).

The *Panzerbefehlswagen Ausf E* was replaced on the assembly lines by the *Panzerbefehlswagen Ausf H* based on the Ausf H tank chassis. Production commenced, still by Daimler-Benz, from November 1940 until September 1931. Such was the demand for these command vehicles that a second batch of 30 was produced during December 1941 and January 1942, the second 30 bringing the total Ausf H command vehicle total up to 145. This Ausf H model carried over the three radio suite options carried by the Ausf E command vehicle.

From the Polish campaign onwards command vehicle users requested better armament for their platforms than just a single machine gun. It was late 1942 before their requests were met, this time not by manufacturing new vehicles but by modifying early production Panzer III Ausf J

tanks armed with the 5cm KwK L/42 gun in a fully traversing turret. Once again, there was no front machine gun installation, just a pistol port. The necessary changes were initially introduced on the Daimler-Benz production lines with 81 examples being delivered between August and November 1942.

By that stage of the war, the manufacture of special command vehicles was regarded as a low priority measure so all subsequent Panzer III command vehicles were thereafter conversions of existing models. The L/42 gun model conversion, once again involving Daimler-Benz, mainly involved the installation of extra command net radios in place of an ammunition rack (this reduced the number of 50mm rounds carried to 75), and the usual frame aerial array was replaced by whip antennae. The usual tank net FuSprGer 5 radio was retained, the extra radio being either a ground-to-air FuSprGer 7 or a divisional link FuSprGer 8. The final 104 conversions were completed, making a total of 185 of this Ausf H variant.

The provision of 185 of the Ausf H command tanks could still not fully meet demands from the field so between December 1942 and February 1943 a further 50 gun tanks were earmarked as command tanks, this time on the Ausf M

production lines. The subsequent model had some minor changes from the standard Ausf M, such as a smaller gun mantlet and extra vision and pistol ports along the superstructure sides, and one major change with the fitting of a modified Panzer IV turret leading to the provision of a new model designation. This was *Panzerbefehlswagen Ausf K*, the last of the Panzer III command vehicles, the original order for 80 of this model being reduced to 50 as the Panzer III production lines were wound down.

Being based on the Ausf M tank, the Ausf K command vehicle, still a Daimler-Benz responsibility, was armed with the long-barrelled 5cm KwK 39 L/60, with stowage for 65 rounds. As with other Panzer III command vehicles, there was no hull machine gun. The radio installation was the usual FuSprGer 5 plus either a FuSprGer 7 or FuSprGer 8.

Flamethrowers

The Battle of Stalingrad had a profound impact on the German armed forces. From that battle emanated all manner of operational or tactical changes together with equipment demands to meet similar future combat scenarios.

Among the equipment demands were calls for a flamethrower tank with a better performance than the limited performance flamethrower platforms then available. These demands were met by delivering the final Panzer III production batch armed accordingly.

The final 100 Panzer III Ausf M chassis were completed by MIAG and passed to Wegmann at Kassel for the necessary *Flammenwerfer* (flame-thrower) equipment to be installed. This equipment, specifically designed for installation in the Panzer III Ausf M, involved a 1.5m (4.92ft) long flame delivery tube mounted in place of the usual main gun armament. The actual flame nozzle had a diameter of 14mm (0.55in) and was connected via internal piping to two internal tanks with a maximum capacity of 1,000ltr (220gal) of *Flammöl* (flame fuel). The fuel tank installation reduced the crew to just three (commander who was also the *Flammenwerfer* operator seated in the cupola position, radio operator/bow machine gunner, and driver). A co-axial machine gun was provided. The electrically ignited flame discharger had a combat range of from 55 to 60m (180.44 to 196.85ft), firing 70 to 80 flame jets each lasting two or three seconds – that was when everything was working properly and under suitable environmental conditions.

Above:
The Panzer III (Fl) with the usual main gun replaced by a *Flammenwerfer* flame gun. This vehicle is a Panzer III Ausf M. *(TM)*

There were delivery delays regarding the *Flammenwerfer* equipment so Wegmann could not start work until February 1943, too late for the completed vehicles to be used at Stalingrad. The last of the batch of 100 (chassis numbers 77609-77708) was completed during April 1943. They were designated as Panzer III (Fl) (SdKfz 141/3) with the (Fl) denoting *Flammenwerfer*.

With no precise tactical application in prospect the flame tanks were delivered to several Panzer battalions where they formed flame-thrower platoons. It is known that 41 examples took part in the fighting around the Kursk salient in July 1943 and several were also used in Italy.

Artillery observation

Following the introduction of 105mm *Wespe* (Wasp) and 155mm *Hummel* (Bumble Bee) fully-tracked armoured artillery vehicles to the *Wehrmacht* there arose a need for armoured forward observation vehicles to spot targets for them. Long-term plans to develop a special vehicle for this role were prepared but as an interim solution it was decided to convert Panzer III Ausf E to Ausf H tanks for the artillery observation role from early 1943 onwards. The tanks involved in the conversion programme were originally armed with the superseded 5cm KwK L/42 gun so diverting them to the artillery observation role extended their useful service lives at no great cost.

By the time this conversion programme had been completed, 268 tanks had been converted to *Artillerie-Panzerbeobachtungswagen* (Panzer III SdKfz 143), usually abbreviated to PzBeobWg. The conversion mainly involved removing the ineffective gun and replacing it with a MG 34 machine gun - the front hull machine gun was removed and its aperture plugged. An offset dummy gun barrel was added to an up-armoured mantlet to disguise the vehicle's lack of gun armament to an enemy. Armoured protection was brought up to

30mm (1.18in) standard all round. As the artillery communications networks worked over different radio frequencies to the Panzer formations, the radio installation was also altered. One of the sets was the FuSprGer 8, as used with some command tanks, plus the FuSprGer 4 artillery control radio that could be removed from the vehicle for remote operation at a ground observation position. The roof had provision for mounting various types of artillery observation binocular.

The last of 268 conversions was completed during April 1944, 225 during 1943 and the remaining 43 during 1944.

Deep wading

With the Battle of France won, by July 1940 the Wehrmacht began making plans for Operation *Seelöwe* (Sealion), the planned amphibious invasion of Great Britain. Tanks were expected to play a major role during the beach landing phase of this operation so a submersion kit was designed for application to both Panzer III and Panzer IV tanks, in both gun and command forms. The Panzer III models involved were a mix of Ausf F, G and H.

For the Panzer III series the result was the *Tauchpanzer III*. It was intended that the prepared tanks would enter the water from suitably equipped landing craft located some distance from the shore. The tanks would then travel up to 15m (49.21ft) beneath the surface and over the sea bottom towards the shore, guidance being given by a gyro compass. All apertures and vulnerable joints between plates were carefully sealed, the turret/superstructure interface being sealed using an inflatable rubber ring. Air was drawn into either the turret or engine by a long flexible hose with a float at its extreme end to keep the end of the hose above the sea surface.

Needless to say, the *Tauchpanzer III* development and training programmes were not entirely trouble free, even experienced tank crews facing their submerged travels with some

Above:
The late version of the submersible *Tauchpanzer III* with a rigid *Schnorkel* tube (mounted on the cupola) undergoing trials. This example is a converted Panzer III Ausf F still armed with a 3.7cm gun. *(TM)*

Right:
A *Bergepanzer III* armoured recovery vehicle. For this role the gun turret was removed and the added superstructure carried various items of recovery equipment. *(TM)*

Below:
A *Bergepanzer III* armoured recovery vehicle towing a *Panzerberganker (1 achs)* anchoring assembly employed when recovering stranded vehicles heavier than the towing vehicle. The drawing shows how this assembly was to be used in action. *(TM)*

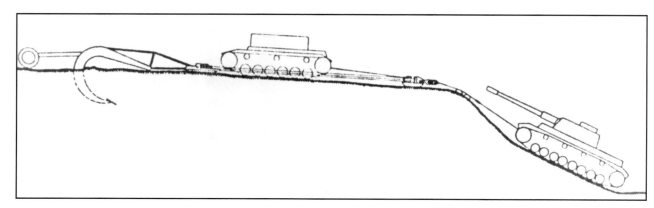

trepidation. Nevertheless, by October 1940 some 168 Tauchpanzer III vehicles and their crews were ready for action, but only after *Seelöwe* had been indefinitely postponed.

The prepared vehicles were therefore used for river crossing operations, such as the crossing of the River Bug during June 1941. As the anticipated river depths were less than those expected under the English Channel, the flexible hose intakes were dispensed with and a fixed *Schnorkel* steel pipe leading to the turret was substituted.

The entire *Tauchpanzer III* project had been suspended by the end of 1941.

Armoured recovery vehicles

By early 1944 it had been decided that the Panzer III tank series no longer had any viable combat role, although there were still appreciable numbers in the *Wehrmacht* inventory. It was therefore decreed that any battle-worn Panzer III gun tanks returned

for major overhaul would be converted to act as armoured recovery vehicles as the *Bergepanzer III*.

The main change for this role was the removal of the turret and its replacement by a large wooden box body to carry tools, recovery equipment and other useful items for the recovery role. Space under the box was occupied by a winch and its cable. A small crane derrick could be erected over the engine compartment covers and the use of wider *Ostkette* track shoes to improve traction was a widespread practice.

When recovering heavy stranded vehicles the *Bergepanzer III* was meant to be used in conjunction with a large and cumbersome anchoring assembly known as a *Panzerberganker* (*1 achs*). This was normally towed on its single two-wheeled axle (*achs*) and lowered to dig into the ground to act as a firm stabilising anchor when the vehicle winch was used to pull a stranded load using the necessary blocks and cables.

Between March and December 1944 a total of 150 Panzer III gun tanks were converted to act as *Bergepanzer* within Panzer IV and *Sturmgeschütz* formations. Their usual crew was

Above:
The raised suspension indicates that this vehicle is the outlandish-looking *Minenräumer III* mine-clearing vehicle intended to push a boom carrying mine-clearing charges across a minefield. It could also push heavy mine-clearing rollers. It remained a prototype. This is a rear view. *(TG)*

Above:
A typical
Munitionspanzer III
armoured supply
vehicle. For this role
the Panzer III turret
was removed and
the resultant area
covered over to carry
ammunition and other
combat supplies to
front line units. The
original vehicle shown
here could have been
either a Panzer III
Ausf F, G or H. *(TM)*

three: a driver and two skilled recovery fitters. Two machine guns were carried, the usual MG 34 installation in the front hull and another for air defence or dismounted use.

Another related Panzer III conversion resulted in the little known and awkwardly named *Instandsetzungskraftswagen*. These were turretless retired Panzer III tanks used as mobile maintenance and repair centres within Panzer formations. Their internal area was occupied by extra batteries to start stranded vehicles, a welding kit, various tools and a supply of the more frequently required spares.

Mine clearing

As far as can be determined there was just one example of the so-called *Minenräumer III* mine-clearing vehicle. This turretless vehicle was supposed to push a boom across a mined area to be cleared before lowering it to leave a string of explosive charges which, when detonated, were meant to destroy any land mines in the immediate vicinity, thereby

clearing a path for others to use. To protect the crew, probably only two, from the danger of mine damage this vehicle had an extensively modified, strengthened and raised suspension that raised the belly armour, no doubt considerably reinforced, well above the terrain surface and away from any mine explosion. In addition to the detonating charge boom, the *Minenräumer III* could also push heavy mine clearing rollers.

The *Minenräumer III* remained a prototype.

Carriers

The least involved of the Panzer III gun tank conversions intended to make the maximum use of otherwise redundant tanks were turretless equipment or ammunition carriers.

The ammunition carrier was the *Munitionspanzer III*, carrying various ammunition loads into the front line areas for Panzer and self-propelled artillery formations. Extra loads could be towed on a sledge. The so-called

Above:
The vehicle in the foreground awaiting take-over by the Norwegian Army during 1945 is a typical *Munitions-panzer III*. (TM)

Left:
Note the array of helmets and the lack of a hull machine gun on this *Munitions-panzer III*. (TM)

Poland 1939 (note yellow Balkenkreuz)
Scale 1:35

Standard Wehrmacht grey (11th Panzer Division marking on side)
Scale 1:35

Winter camouflage, France 1940
Scale 1:35

© 2003 John Batchelor.

Left:
Taken from the pages of *Signal* (Hitler's lavishly produced magazine for the German forces), this photograph shows *Panzergrenadiers* taking cover behind a PzKpfw III. *(BA)*

Pionierpanzer III was slightly more involved as it had racks to carry small assault bridges, bridge components or boats and other combat engineer equipment.

These relatively cheap and simple carrier conversions were carried out from May 1943 until May 1944. Conversions were probably carried out at field workshop facilities so exact numbers have not been discovered. The turrets left over following such conversions were assigned for fixed fortifications. By 1944 that usually meant the *Atlantikwall*.

Railway

Another Panzer III variant destined to remain at the prototype stage was the *Schienen-Kampfwagen 1* (SK1), a Panzer III Ausf N converted to run on railway tracks. By 1943 Soviet Partisan activity was seriously disrupting German railway supply networks so the SK1 was proposed as an adjunct to defensive *Panzerzüge* (armoured trains).

The SK1 ran on two railway axles that were raised up into the lower hull when it was necessary to run the vehicle on its tracks. Power for the rail axles was provided by a take-off from the tank engine, the reduced rail track friction enabling a maximum speed of up to 100km/h (62mph). The development work for this rail system was carried out at the Saurer-Werke in Vienna but the project did not advance beyond two or three prototypes.

Air defence

During late 1944 the Allied air superiority over all fronts was such that increasing demands

were raised for more and more air defence tanks, or *Flakpanzer*. One proposed partial solution was seen as modified 20mm or 37mm air defence gun turrets, normally carried by *Flakpanzer IV* series air defence tanks, placed on any available Panzer III chassis and hulls. Trials were held during early 1945 and 90 retired tank chassis were assigned for conversion to become the *Flakpanzer III*, but the end of the war terminated the programme.

Assault gun

During battles around Stalingrad in late 1942, the Soviets captured significant numbers of Panzer III gun tanks. Being desperately short of all manner of combat equipment following their huge losses sustained during 1941 and 1942, it made sense for the Soviets to utilise these captured vehicles against the *Wehrmacht*. In addition, the Soviet's SU-76 mobile 76mm gun carriers were unreliable experiencing a series of mechanical failures, leading to severe front-line shortages at a time where such equipments were badly needed.

It was therefore decided to utilise captured Panzer III tanks as self-propelled artillery platforms for the then readily available 76.2mm S-1 tank gun (a simplified variant of the widely used F-34 tank gun). Work on the project started in February 1943, the development period lasting just one month before 'production' could start at Factory No.37 at Sverdlovsk. A total of 181 conversions were completed, plus 20 command variants fitted with an extra radio, with ammunition stowage reduced to less than the usual 98 rounds. The first of these conversions reached the front

Above:
An early *Sturmgeschütz* (StuG Ausf D or E) assault gun (SdKfz 142) on a Panzer III Ausf F chassis. It is armed with a 7.5cm KwK L/33. *(ID)*

77

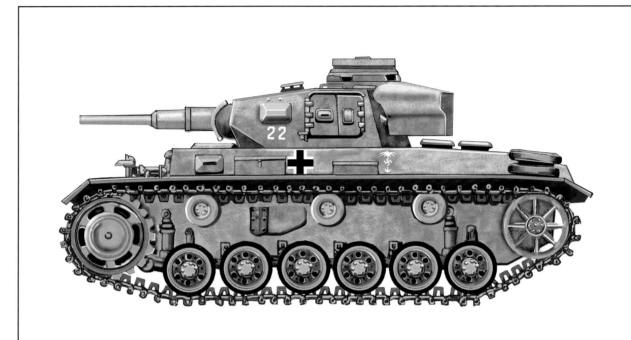

Afrika Korps desert camouflage
Scale 1:35

© 2003 Mike Rose.

Afrika Korps Libya camouflage
Scale 1:35

© 2003 Mike Rose.

Eastern Front camouflage, 1943
Scale 1:35

© 2003 Mike Rose.

CHAPTER SEVEN

ORGANISATION

During the early war years the Panzer III formed the backbone of the Panzer formations and it carried the main combat burdens from 1940 until 1943, although by the end of this period it was well outclassed for armoured warfare.

The Panzer division was not an all-tank formation but a highly mobile self-contained combat team capable of operating independently using only its own resources. In addition to its tank complement, each division had two or three battalions of motorised infantry (in some cases four), known as *Panzergrenadier*, a motorcycle battalion, a motorised artillery battalion, an anti-tank battalion, a reconnaissance battalion equipped with armoured cars and motor-cycles, and a combat engineer battalion, plus logistics, medical, signals and other support units.

Although the invasion of Poland took place in September 1939 the bulk of the tank formations employed were equipped only with the Panzer I or Panzer II, plus numbers of captured Czech-built tanks. The Panzer III was then not available in sufficient numbers to play any significant part in the invasion.

When the first Panzer III units went into action during the Battle of France in May and June 1940 they were organised within the Panzer Division armoured brigades. Each division contained an armoured brigade that was meant to have four battalions, although some had only three battalions. Three divisions were equipped with captured Czech tanks (PzKpfw 35 [t] and PzKpfw 38 [t]) following the final take-over of Czechoslovakia during early 1939.

On paper, a tank battalion was meant to have four companies, of which three formed the combat element - the fourth was a headquarters, administration, replacement and support company. Two of the companies were equipped with the Panzer III, the third with the Panzer IV acting primarily in the fire support role. Each tank company had a nominal 22 tanks, although this total was rarely maintained due to the perennial shortfalls in German tank production and delivery from 1940 onwards. These shortages reduced tank strength within some divisions to three and eventually to just two battalions. As the war progressed some divisions could not be completely equipped with tanks so *Sturmgeschütz* (StuG) assault guns, along with *Panzerjäger* tank destroyers once they appeared, were employed in their place.

The appearance of the T-34 meant that the Panzer III became obsolete (cont. page 92)

Above:
A late production Panzer III Ausf N armed with the short 7.5cm KwK L/24 main gun. Note the absence of an escape hatch in the hull side. *(TM)*

Left:
A Panzer III Ausf G crossing a river during the early phases of Operation *Barbarossa*, the invasion of the Soviet Union during 1941. The 'K' on the hull front indicates that this vehicle was part of Army Group Kleist. *(TM)*

Above:
The fully restored late production example of a Panzer III Ausf L held by the Tank Museum at Bovington, Dorset, England. *(TM)*

Right:
Three-quarters rear view of the Tank Museum's production Panzer III Ausf L showing revised engine covers and the turret basket. *(TM)*

Above:
The spaced armour over the turret gun mantlet and the front plate gives extra protection to the driver and hull MG gunner. *(TM)*

Left:
Rear view of the same Panzer III Ausf L. Note how the sides of the turret basket have been cut away to allow an arc of fire from the pistol ports in the back of the turret. *(TM)*

Above:
Visible on the rear of
the commander's
cupola on this Panzer
III Ausf E is the tactical
sign of the 12th
Panzer Division. This
illustration almost
certainly dates from
the 1940 campaign
in France - note the
Panzerwaffe beret was
only worn in the early
campaigns. *(TM)*

Right:
A Panzer III Ausf E
displaying the
Buffalo emblem
of the 10th Panzer
Division on the rear
of the cupola. *(TM)*

Above:
The Panzer III Ausf E or F in the foreground of this picture, probably dating from the invasion of the Soviet Union during 1941, carries an extra turret basket displaying the prominent 'K' of Army Group Kleist. *(HW)*

Left:
Close up of the flap for the driver's side vision flap showing the *Ersatzgläser* (synthetic armoured glass) block on a Panzer III Ausf L. The tactical sign is for the 15th Panzer Division. *(TG)*

Standard Wehrmacht grey (3rd Panzer Division marking on side)
Scale 1:35

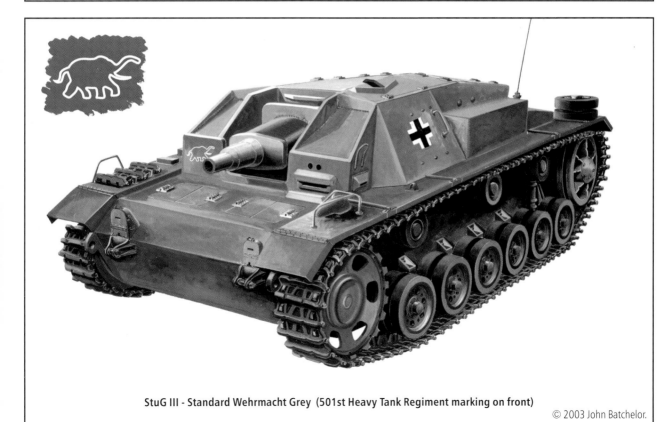

StuG III - Standard Wehrmacht Grey (501st Heavy Tank Regiment marking on front)

Turret Numbers, colour and outline variations

Tactical Signs 1935-42

Panzer Div HQ

Panzer Div CP

Panzer Brigade HQ

1st Panzer Regiment

2nd Panzer Regiment

4th Panzer Battalion (I/I-II/2)

Staff Co.

Medium Tank Company

Armoured Workshop Company

Tactical Signs 1943-45

Panzer Division HQ

Panzer Regiment HQ

Staff Co.

Panzer Abteilungen (Panzer Battalions)

Armoured Supply Co.

Armoured Workshop Co.

StuG III Co.

Armoured Engineer Battalion HQ

Right:
A Panzergrenadier
takes cover behind a
Panzer III as another
tank goes into action
against the enemy
in a Russian village,
1941. *(BA)*

Below:
Senior officers of the
Panzerwaffe hold a
meeting to discuss a
forthcoming attack
against a target in
Russia, 1941. *(BA)*

as a combat tank so by 1943 the place of the
Panzer III within the Panzer battalions was
gradually assumed by the Panzer IV, and the
Panzer V as this more advanced tank appeared.
The Panzer III series remained an element of
the Panzer formations only in the form of the
associated *Sturmgeschütz* and some other self-
propelled artillery equipments. Well
before 1943 the number of tank battalions
within the Panzer divisions had fallen to
two or, in the case of the light divisions,
just one. This reduction, unpopular with
many armoured staff officers as it reduced their
striking power, made internal organisation
more flexible, the tank shortfalls being partially
balanced by increases in motorised infantry and
artillery strengths. Part of the reason for the
reduction measures was once again the general
shortage of German tanks.

Some Panzer III units remained in service
until the end of the war in 1945 but by then
they were rear area patrol or reserve training
units only, their vehicles destined to be
converted for a variety of purposes when
opportunity arose.

Left:
A snow camouflaged
Panzer III Ausf L -
note the absence of
a hull escape hatch
which suggests this
is probably a late
production example.
(TM)

Below:
Cavalry from two eras
meet as Soviet soldiers
examine a captured
Panzer III Ausf G. *(TM)*

Panzer Division signs, 1939-1945

1940   1941-45   1940-45

——— 1st Panzer Division ———

1939-40   1940   1941-43   1943-45

——— 2nd Panzer Division ———

1940   1941-45   1941-45   1941-45

——— 3rd Panzer Division ———

1939   1940   1941-45   1943   1940   1941-45

——— 4th Panzer Division ———   ——— 5th Panzer Division ———

1940   1941-45   1941

——— 6th Panzer Division ———

1940   1940   1941-45   1943-45   1940   1941-45

——— 7th Panzer Division ———   ——— 8th Panzer Division ———

© 2003 Nigel Pell.